UNDER THE HILL
And Other Essays
in Prose and Verse by Aubrey
BEARDSLEY

with a
new introduction by
Edward Lucie-Smith

PADDINGTON
Masterpieces of the
Illustrated Book

Library of Congress Cataloging in Publication Data

Beardsley, Aubrey Vincent, 1872–1898.
  Under the hill.

  (Masterpieces of the illustrated book)

  Reprint of the 1904 ed. published by J. Lane, London, issued under
  title: Under the hill and other essays in prose and verse.
  CONTENTS: Under the hill.—The three musicians.—The ballad of a
  barber.—Translation of Catullus: Carmen CL. [etc.]
  I. Title.
PR4089.B45U6 1977   824'.8   77-5506
ISBN 0-448-22063-6

Printed in England by Balding & Mansell Ltd., Wisbech, Cambs.

IN THE UNITED STATES
PADDINGTON PRESS LTD.
Distributed by
GROSSET & DUNLAP

IN THE UNITED KINGDOM
PADDINGTON PRESS LTD.

IN CANADA
Distributed by
RANDOM HOUSE OF CANADA LTD.

IN AUSTRALIA
Distributed by
ANGUS & ROBERTSON PTY. LTD.

IN SOUTHERN AFRICA
Distributed by
ERNEST STANTON (PUBLISHERS) (PTY.) LTD.

UNDER THE HILL
And Other Essays
in Prose and Verse by Aubrey
BEARDSLEY

Aubrey Beardsley and *Under the Hill*

During the past ten years there has been an intense revival of interest in Aubrey Beardsley's work, sparked off, at least in England, by the extremely comprehensive retrospective exhibition mounted by the Victoria and Albert Museum in London in 1966. At that time an unconscious tribute was paid to the ambiguity of the artist's reputation. The organizers of the show decided to exhibit the erotic drawings made by Beardsley to illustrate the de luxe edition of Aristophanes' *Lysistrata*, published by Leonard Smithers in 1896. Some reproductions of these drawings appeared in the window of a nearby bookseller, and were promptly confiscated by the police. Beardsley, it seemed, still had the power to shock which he had exercised so gleefully and so often in his own lifetime.

But there was another aspect to the matter which passed largely unnoticed. Sometimes, when an original of this kind is reproduced commercially, the coarsening inherent in the processes of reproduction removes a large part of the aesthetic pleasure we can derive from it, and leaves us face-to-face with its less acceptable qualities. In this case, the cheap reproductions which the bookseller put on view were by no means travesties, but preserved intact all the important qualities of the originals. The reason for this was Beardsley's own artistic attitude. Almost everything he drew was expressly designed to suit the processes available to him, and his medium was the newly invented technique of the photo line-block. This, with its hard, linear precision and total absence of intermediate tones, set the terms for what has come to be called the "Beardsley style." Seeming to cater for a limited and highly sophisticated public, Beardsley was in fact the first draughtsman to understand the implications of an important technological innovation.

His first great opportunity as an artist, and the commission which established his reputation, was for a new edition of Malory's *Morte D'Arthur*, published in parts by J. M. Dent in 1893–4. When they

decided to risk giving this important job to a young unknown, Dents
were perfectly clear in their own minds as to what they wanted.
They wanted to do something in the style of William Morris's
Kelmscott Press, but at a popular price. And, of course, in order to
manage this, they had to abandon the Kelmscott principle of hand
production. Beardsley filled the bill because he was able to use the
techniques they had available to give them something which looked
not unlike a Burne-Jones woodcut.

It has been observed by the historians of technology that a new
invention often gains acceptance with the public by disguising itself
as something familiar. Thus the automobile, which was an exciting
innovation to Beardsley and his contemporaries, was more readily
acceptable as the "horseless carriage"; and the internal combustion
engine was used to power vehicles which were very similar in form to
those drawn by horses. The photo line-block, as Beardsley first used
it, took on an equally familiar guise. But he was not an artist who
could content himself with this kind of mock-medieval pastiche.

Throughout his adult life, Beardsley knew himself to be a mortally
sick man, and the impatient rhythm of his development reflects his
consciousness that there was little time to lose. The *Morte D'Arthur*
commission, though he grew extremely weary of it, gave him a
thorough grounding in the necessities not only of illustration, but of
ornamental design, since the elaborate initials and borders were also
his work. The commission to illustrate Oscar Wilde's biblical play
Salome, which marked the next stage in his progress, showed a great
advance in originality, since here the illustration and decoration
become one and the same. The designs are significant in other ways
as well. There is, for example, the earliest statement of a theme
which was to continue to fascinate the artist — that of a woman's
toilet. Two very different versions of it — "The Toilet of Helen" and
"The Coiffing" — make their appearance in this book. And there are
also instances of Beardsley's habit of turning a set of illustrations into
a kind of sub-text. The caricatures of Wilde which appear in several
of the *Salome* illustrations add a strange little obbligato of their own.

In one sense, however, the *Salome* drawings have done a disservice to Beardsley's reputation, and have tended to cloud people's conception of the way in which he developed. It was through this extraordinary set of illustrations that the English Arts and Crafts sensibility, and late Pre-Raphaelitism in general, found themselves transformed into something very different, and fundamentally opposite in aim — the international and largely Beardsley-inspired decorative style which came to be known as Art Nouveau. The cover-design used by John Lane for the first edition of *Under the Hill*, and printed here on page 17, was itself first intended for *Salome*, and its waving peacock's feathers are an instantly recognizable example of Art Nouveau design at its most inventive and powerful. But the contents of the book, text and illustrations alike, belong to a very different category.

Art Nouveau was proud of its break with the past, though it acknowledged the influence of Japanese decorative design, and also of Japanese *Ukiyo-e* prints. "The Toilet of Salome" owes a clear debt to some of Utamaro's compositions; in the stunning illustration called "The Black Cape," Utamaro's personality is yet more obvious. But by the time he came to do the illustrations which appear in *Under the Hill*, Beardsley had largely worked his way through and absorbed this almost overwhelming Eastern influence. The sources of the pictures here are far more varied and complex, and offer an accurate reflection of the rich variety of sources, both literary and visual, which Beardsley was now able to draw upon.

I say "both literary and visual" because it is one of the fascinations of this particular volume that the contents are all Beardsley — words as well as illustrations. There is no question here of the illustrator undermining and even to some extent subverting the text that accompanies his designs. Everything comes from the same mind. It is true, of course, that Beardsley's literary gifts have not aroused the same degree of admiration as his artistic ones. The main text in *Under the Hill* is the unfinished novel of the same title which in turn derives from the longer, but also unfinished, *Story of Venus and*

Tannhäuser. The Yellow Book, the periodical with which Beardsley was then connected as art-editor, carried an advertisement for the latter in 1894, and the book was supposed to make its appearance the next year, accompanied by no fewer than twenty-four illustrations.

There seem to have been several reasons for the non-appearance of the story in the form originally planned. The most compelling was Beardsley's increasingly poor health, which left him physically incapable of producing the number of illustrations required, especially at the rate needed for periodical publication. Another was Beardsley's dismissal from *The Yellow Book* and parting from John Lane, as a result of the Oscar Wilde scandal. A third was the nature of the text itself. Not only was it "obscene" by the prurient standards of the time, but it was overloaded with digressions, and lacked narrative impulse. Beardsley was enough of a writer to know that it would benefit from stringent revision. *Under the Hill*, which finally made its appearance in the first two numbers of *The Savoy*, in 1896, is generally thought of as being simply the expurgated version of the earlier story. But, though still only a fragment, it is also a far more finished and satisfactory work of art, and in many respects more important than historians of literature have been willing to admit.

The basic myth is still that of Venus and her mortal lover Tannhäuser. This may have appealed to Beardsley for very personal reasons — because it incorporated his own attraction towards a luxurious sinfulness and diabolism, and at the same time his feeling (justified in the event) that he would in the end return to the consolations of religion. For the artist and most of his contemporaries the story was most accessible as the plot of Wagner's opera *Tannhäuser*, and the decision to use it was a somewhat ambiguous tribute to the mania for Wagner's music. By the time the second version came to be written, however, Beardsley had decided to change the names of the two principal characters. Venus becomes Helen; and Tannhäuser, more surprisingly, becomes the dandified Abbé Fanfreluche. As Brigid Brophy points out in her recent perceptive study of Beardsley, the word "abbé" is a pun — Beardsley's initials A. B. have the same sound if pronounced in the French fashion. There was even an intervening stage in the process of rewriting when the character was called the Abbé Aubrey. Beardsley therefore pictures himself transported to an imaginary realm where every fantasy can be fulfilled, though retribution must inevitably follow. The atmosphere of the magic domain within the mountain remains as strongly erotic as it ever was, though the eroticism is no longer as explicit as it had been in the first version.

In the long dedicatory preface, addressed to a fictional "Cardinal of the Holy Roman Church," Beardsley carefully dictates to us the way we should read his main text. The model for this preface is eighteenth-century — exemplified by the writing of Lord Chesterfield. Its tone tells us that whatever follows must be viewed by the reader with a suitably distancing irony:

Still, as the book will be found to contain matter of deeper import than mere venery, inasmuch as it treats of the great contribution of its chiefest character, and of canonical things in certain pages, I am not without hopes that your Eminence will pardon me writing of a loving Abbé, for which extravagance let my youth excuse me.

Wagner's mystical material is filtered through the author's extensive experience of the English and French literature of the century preceding his own. There are clear traces of the "libertine" novels produced by authors such as Restif de la Bretonne, and these echoes produce fascinating and ambiguous contrasts of tone. But *Under the Hill* is a long way from being a mere pastiche, though the author uses parody as one of his literary weapons. The highly wrought, totally individual style — on the first page of the narrative, for example, the Abbé is found "quelling the little mutinies of cravat and ruffle" — was to provide the chief model for the novels which Ronald Firbank was to write a couple of decades later. Because of the half-mocking, half-believing attitude to Catholicism which the two writers have in common, there is a particular resemblance to Firbank's masterpiece, *The Eccentricities of Cardinal Pirelli*, published in 1926. Beardsley's ironic footnote on St. Rose of Lima, in Chapter IV, is precisely in Firbank's manner. This connection is important for two reasons. The first is that Firbank is generally held to be the starting-point of a now established tradition in the English comic novel. It is a tradition which embraces the early work of Evelyn Waugh, that of Anthony Powell (whose second novel, published in 1932, is entitled *Venusberg*), and also many of the novels of Muriel Spark, including the recent fantasy *The Abbess of Crewe*. The Wagner opera which is the immediate parent of *Under the Hill* is written in the upholstered, totally humorless style we might expect; and it is pleasant to think that, through the agency of Beardsley's genius, it managed to spawn so numerous and so thoroughly irreverent a progeny.

The second reason for studying the text of *Under the Hill* is that it is the foundation-stone of Beardsley's claim to be the originator of the cult of "camp." Camp began life as a theatrical term, denoting an ironically exaggerated mode of behavior. In the 1960s the word came into general use, and its implications were examined by Susan Sontag and other critics. Their conclusion was that "camp" now meant a confusion of aesthetic genres — what had pretensions to seriousness was lightly dismissed, what was generally regarded as trashy was made the subject of serious study and admiration. Beardsley, of all late-nineteenth-century authors, shows the closest approximation to camp qualities, as they have been subsequently defined. This was perhaps due to the tragedy of his personal situation. At the time when *Under the Hill* was written, and indeed long before, he knew himself to be a dying man. On the one hand there were those friends, such as the homosexual couple André Raffalovich and Father John Gray, who tried to draw him towards the Catholic Church; on the other were men such as his disreputable publisher Leonard Smithers, who encouraged the rebellious sensuality associated with his disease — tuberculosis. Beardsley's conflicting feelings about his way of life and its approaching end were partly resolved by his seriously frivolous treatment of personages such as "Saint Rose, the well-known Peruvian virgin."

The drawing with which Beardsley chose to illustrate this particular passage was one which he considered to be one of his best; and its mingling of overt sensuality with genuine mystical feeling certainly makes it striking. We can see from it that Beardsley, as he was drawn towards Catholicism, was also quick to learn from the elegant excesses of late Baroque religious art. Yet, since he never traveled to Bavaria, it is highly probable that he had never seen the work of the great Rococo sculptor Ignaz Gunther, which this composition, despite the difference of medium, so closely resembles. What Gunther achieves is the combination of genuine fervor with a kind of smiling and ironic courtliness. His saints are *grandes dames* even at the moment of martyrdom. Beardsley achieves a similar solution to one of the most difficult of aesthetic problems, which is that of expressing mystical union with God without making it seem ridiculous.

If St. Rose of Lima gives us one aspect of his art, other illustrations to *Under the Hill* are quite different both in manner and in content, and give a glimpse of the immensely wide range of Beardsley's culture. The first, of the Abbé Fanfreluche, owes a good deal to the illustrations to be found in de luxe editions of French eighteenth-century *contes galantes*, but the source material is transformed by Beardsley's momentary *horror vacui*, which leads him to reinterpret it in the manner of one of the monumental Passion woodcuts by Dürer. The second plate, "The Toilet of Helen," is, as I have already said, an ambitious new version of a favorite theme. It is close in manner to Beardsley's illustrations for Pope's *The Rape of the Lock*, but with an added grotesquerie, more Renaissance than eighteenth-century, which is due to the capering figures of the dwarves in the foreground. Miss Marsuple, Helen's hideous confidante, who appears in profile at the right, seems to be a reworking of the older of the two figures in Beardsley's frontispiece to Flaubert's *Education Sentimentale*, drawn in

1894. This, in turn, offers a commentary on the relationship between the young woman and the older one. The third illustration, "The Fruit Bearers," is in some respects the most interesting of all, if we look at it in relation to the development of Beardsley's late style.

Towards the end of his brief life — he died in 1898 aged twenty-seven — Beardsley showed an increasing interest in the art of the Italian Renaissance, and in that of Mantegna in particular. The photograph showing Beardsley at the Hotel Cosmopolitan, Mentone, in the room in which he died, shows one wall virtually covered with reproductions of engravings by Mantegna and his school. Beardsley was aware of the work of other Italian engravers and illustrators as well. The designs for the frontispiece and title page of the original story of *Venus and Tannhäuser* demonstrate the impact on him of the woodcuts in the famous Venetian allegorical romance, the *Hypnerotomachia Poliphili*, first published in 1499 and republished in facsimile (the medium through which Beardsley knew it) in 1889. But it is clear, not only from "The Fruit Bearers," but from the set of illustrations and initial letters for Ben Jonson's *Volpone* (which he failed to complete because he was too ill) that his taste was moving toward the severest kind of Renaissance classicism — a heavy style far removed from the work he had done when he was first making his reputation.

It is for this reason that the *Rheingold* illustration sits rather uneasily among the others in *Under the Hill*. In fact, this belongs properly speaking to an earlier, Art Nouveau cycle, a set of illustrations to the first of the "Ring" operas. When Beardsley was too ill to make the required quota of illustrations for the second installment of his story on its appearance in *The Savoy* in 1896, he threw in this as a makeweight, using as his excuse a passing reference to the work in his text.

In common with nearly all the artists and writers connected with the Symbolist Movement, Beardsley seems to have been fascinated by Wagner's music, though the best of all his drawings provoked by this stimulus, "The Wagnerites," shows a thoroughly decadent-looking and almost entirely female audience listening to the music of *Tristan und Isolde*. Wagner represents, so to speak, one extreme of Beardsley's taste, one frontier of his capacity to react to works of art, and "The Wagnerites" is a comment concerned with his knowledge of his own reactions, and all the more interesting for that. Love–hate was always a fruitful emotion so far as Beardsley was concerned.

Some of the remaining illustrations were made in connection with Beardsley's own poems, and the texts reveal his limitations as a writer of verse. He achieves in "The Three Musicians" a certain sub-Dowsonian charm, but the two designs (one originally made as an alternative to the other) and the tailpiece are more significant than the poem because they show yet another aspect of his art. The tailpiece is a piece of almost pure *dix-huitièmerie*, but the illustrations are unsure about which period they want to evoke. If the basic mood is that of a Marie-Antoinette pastoral, then many details, particularly those of the boy's costume, suggest an epoch some fifty years later — around 1830 in fact. The revival of interest in the early Romantic period began surprisingly early and Beardsley was partly responsible. We find it evoked is some of the work Bakst and Benois did for Diaghilev, in connection with ballets devised by Fokine, and we find it also in the work of Russian Symbolist painters such as Victor Borissov-Mussatov. Borissov-Mussatov was a pupil of Gustave Moreau, and may have become acquainted with Beardsley's work in Paris.

"The Coiffing" is a much better illustration to what is on the whole a far inferior text. Arthur Symons, who was at that time acting as literary editor of *The Savoy*, and who did not greatly like Beardsley, made a determined effort to keep the Grand Guignol "Ballad of a Barber" out of the magazine. Beardsley resisted, it appears from his correspondence, not so much because he set a great deal of store by the text, but because he was determined to save the picture that went with it. In this endeavor he was quite right. "The Coiffing" is a marvellous specimen of Beardsley's skill. It is worth noting how cunningly recession in space is suggested by the diagonal of the three figures: the statuette of the Madonna on the mantlepiece, then the standing barber with his pursed face, and finally the seated princess. Equally noteworthy is the way in which the artist suggests texture solely by means of lines and dots. The harshest and heaviest lines, for instance, are used for the crisp satin of the girl's sash.

Though this and the picture that accompanies Beardsley's translation of Catullus' famous "Ave atque Vale" are in most respects quite different, the two things they have in common are the control of outline and the use of asymmetry. The figure of the young poet is a reminder of the fact that Beardsley, alone amongst modern artists, was capable of producing outline drawings worthy to be compared with those which make their appearance on the best Greek red-figure vases. Yet this is no copy. A characteristic touch is the deliberate misplacement of the one visible nipple, which not only makes the chest itself look broader but slightly flattens the relief, and keeps the torso in harmony with the despondent profile of the head. The verses themselves have a plangency which makes them perhaps the best things that Beardsley ever wrote.

The only other illustration which requires comment is the frontispiece to John Davidson's *Plays*, which stirred up a certain amount of controversy, as the reader will see from the two letters that accompany the picture in this volume. People recognized the portraits of Oscar Wilde and of the impresario Augustus Harris — it was Harris who "owed" Beardsley half a crown, as the latter had bought a ticket to one of his shows, then failed to get into it. But there are other portraits too — the writer Richard Le Galienne is recognizable, and so is the ballerina Adeline Genée. The naked girl seems to be intended for Beardsley's sister Mabel, with whom he had a particularly intense relationship, which some have thought incestuous. The faun may be intended for Beardsley himself, and the grouping of the three personages on the left-hand side of the composition may be meant to symbolize some long-forgotten intrigue between Mabel and the dionysiac Oscar (whose legs, nevertheless, appear to be fettered as if to suggest his impotence to do anything about it).

The drawing is an especially elaborate example of Beardsley's tendency to import gratuitous private meanings into his work. He terrified all those who employed him by the extreme skill he showed at smuggling in improper details which were bound to shock the sensitive opinion of the time.

Under the Hill is not a book deliberately composed by Beardsley. It is a collection of bits and pieces put together after his death. Yet within its narrow compass it does give a surprisingly complete picture of his artistic personality. Though it is Beardsley the artist who is immortal, we cannot understand him without some reference to Beardsley the writer. And the rather sporadic attempts which Beardsley made at authorship have had, as we have noted, a surprisingly widespread influence. As an artist he is now so popular that he is in some danger of becoming too familiar. It is the texts which help to remind us that below the elegant surface of the drawings a powerful daemon stirs, and will continue to stir so long as people find it worthwhile to look at what he did.

Edward Lucie-Smith

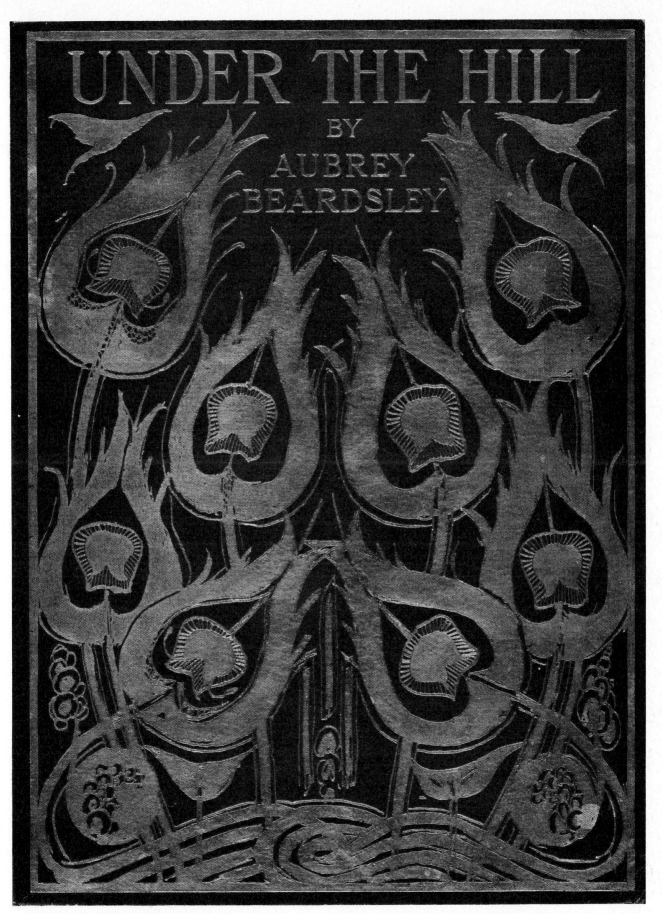

The gold-blocked cover of the first edition, designed by Aubrey Beardsley

Published by Leonard Smithers and Cᵒ 1899.

Aubrey Beardsley at Mentone.

in the room in which he died.

PUBLISHER'S NOTE

To those who are acquainted with Aubrey Beardsley's essays into the domain of literature no apology for this re-publication is needed—indeed Beardsley's most intimate friends have averred that if his master genius had been turned seriously towards the world of letters, his success would have been as undoubted there as it was in the world of art.

Admirers frequently have expressed a wish to see the literary remains of Beardsley. This volume, in which are gathered together various fragments and personalia, will, I trust, meet the case.

A few of my random recollections of Beardsley's association with "The Yellow Book" perhaps will not be amiss.

Until the publication of the first volume of "The Yellow Book" in 1894, Beardsley was practically unknown, his drawings for "Le Morte D'Arthur" and his marvellous designs illustrating "Salome" constituting his artistic record. It was at this time, then, that one morning he, with Mr. Henry Harland and myself, during half an hour's chat over our cigarettes at the Hogarth Club, founded the much discussed "Yellow Book." Beardsley became Art Editor, whilst Mr. Harland accepted the post of Literary Editor.

Many will remember the sensation caused by the appearance of the first volume. Perhaps the *Westminster Gazette* and the *Times* were the most severe in their strictures, at any rate on the Art in general and on Beardsley in particular.

The *Westminster Gazette* said :

"Mr. Aubrey Beardsley achieves excesses hitherto undreamt of. He seems to have conceived the disagreeable idea of taking certain arrangements of lines invented by the Japanese, and specially suited to blithe and pleasant peaks of decoration, and applying them to the most morbid of grotesque. His offence is the less to be condoned because he has undoubted skill as a line draughtsman and has shown himself capable of refined and delicate work. But as regards certain of his inventions in this number, the thing called 'The Sentimental Education,' and that other thing to which the name of Mrs. Patrick Campbell has somehow become attached, we do not know that anything would meet the case except a short Act of Parliament to make this kind of thing illegal."

The *Times* said :

"'The Yellow Book' is, we suppose, destined to be the organ of the New Literature and the New Art. If the New Art is represented by the cover of this wonderful volume, it is scarcely calculated to attract by its intrinsic beauty or merit ; possibly, however, it may be intended to attract by its very repulsiveness and insolence, and in that case it is not unlikely to be successful. Its note appears to be a combination of English rowdyism with French lubricity. . . . Sir Frederick Leighton, who contributes two graceful studies, finds himself cheek by jowl with such advanced and riotous representatives of the New Art as Mr. Aubrey Beardsley and Mr. Walter Sickert.   On the whole the New Art and the New Literature appear to us to compare in this singular volume far from favourably with the old."

It may interest the *Times* critic to know that Sir Frederick Leighton was a great admirer of Beardsley's work.   At one of Sir Frederick's periodical visits to the Bodley Head to see how the New Art and the New Literature were developing, he playfully suggested that if he was not " performing an R.A. duty he was doing a neighbourly one."   He asked to see the originals of Beardsley's " Yellow Book " pictures (Vol. I.), and then remarked : " Ah ! what wonderful line ! What a great artist ! " and then *sotto voce*, " if he could only draw."   My retort was, " Sir Frederick, I am tired of seeing men who can *only* draw."   " Oh ! yes," said Sir Frederick, " I know what you mean, and you are quite right too."

There was indeed a universal howl against the cover and title-page designs, which it will be remembered were both the work of Beardsley.   However the conductors of " The Yellow Book " were nothing daunted and proceeded to announce that for each volume in the future Mr. Beardsley would complete new cover and title-page designs.   This was an entirely fresh idea, and has since been adopted by most of the leading illustrated magazines both in England and America.

An interesting and original contribution to Volume II. of " The Yellow Book," one which did not fulfil its object however, was a criticism of the contents of Volume I. by the late P. G. Hammerton. Mr. Hammerton, being merely an art critic and not a humorist, did not fulfil the commission quite in the spirit in which it was given him ; the conductors of the quarterly desired criticism, even though adverse to themselves. I am sure that nothing would have delighted the two editors more than a good slating in their own pages, but Mr. Hammerton, always conscientious, found nothing but praise for its contents, especially for Beardsley's work.

Beardsley's defect as Art Editor was youth. He would not take himself seriously : as an editor and draughtsman he was almost a practical joker, for one had, so to speak, to place his drawings under a microscope, and look at them upside down. This tendency on the eve of the production of Vol. V., during my first visit to the United States, rendered it necessary to omit his work from that volume.

Beardsley was responsible for the art of the first four volumes, and it must be frankly confessed that, when he severed his connection with the magazine, the quarterly suffered an irretrievable loss.

Soon after this period, Mr. Arthur Symonds started " The Savoy," as a rival, to which Beardsley, again as Art Editor, contributed another fine series of drawings.

I well remember being interviewed in New York regarding the alleged decadence in Beardsley's work. I said then, and repeat now, that he merely lashed the follies of his time, that he was the Hogarth of his day, and that he had no more sympathy with decadence than Hogarth had for the vices depicted in " The Rake's Progress " and " Marriage à la Mode." Knowledge must never be confounded with sympathy. I will go farther, and declare that Beardsley, by his grotesque and powerful pictures of several hideous phases of life, dealt a death blow to decadence. Had he lived till now, it is quite possible that the Royal Academy might have justified its existence by recognising in him the greatest exponent of the most vital of the graphic arts—namely, Black and White. In support of this theory it may be well to point out that Mr. Harland is now the delight of millions by his charming love romances, and that " Max " in his brilliant weekly articles in the *Saturday Review* pleads eloquently for an intelligent drama.

It was not often that Beardsley took up his pen to write to the newspapers, preferring to allow the hostile and adverse criticism with which he was continually assailed to confute themselves. On two occasions, however, he did so, and the letters he wrote will be found included in this volume. The first, I think, with the accompanying illustration, explains itself. The second was the outcome of the following criticism by the *Daily Chronicle*, March 1, 1894, on the frontispiece of Mr. John Davidson's " Plays ' .

" AN ERROR OF TASTE "

" Mr. Beardsley has contributed a frontispiece *à propos* of 'Scaramouch in Naxos' in which one or two well-known faces of the day are to be recognised—an error of taste which is to be regretted."

The subjects of Beardsley's two portraits were Mr. Wilde and Sir Augustus Harris ; the latter Beardsley considered his debtor by virtue of his having taken half a crown at Covent Garden Theatre without providing him with a seat.

Aubrey Beardsley was born on August 21, 1872, and died on March 16, 1898. During his short life he carried the art of Black and White further than any man since Albert Dürer. On his death prophetic assurances were not wanting that the " Beardsley cult " or " craze," as it was generally called, was doomed to extinction with the death of its high priest, but so far from this anticipation being realised, his work now enjoys a greater appreciation and more intelligent sympathy than was granted to it, save by an esoteric few, during his lifetime.

Although it is impossible, with any degree of accuracy, to state to what extent Beardsley's popularity has increased during the last few years, evidence is not wanting to show that his following is both enthusiastic and loyal. This applies not only to Great Britain, but equally to America, whilst in Germany, France, Belgium, Russia and Holland, it is safe to affirm that his reputation is steadily growing, especially in Germany. Indeed, it is obvious to the most superficial observer that there is hardly a Black and White artist working to-day who has not in some subtle way been influenced by the master.

More than three-fourths of Beardsley's work passed through my hands, and to my knowledge he never used Chinese White. I am the fortunate possessor of the originals of over eighty of his principal drawings. I get applications from would-be purchasers of these from different parts of the world almost daily, but as yet I have withstood all temptations to part with these treasures, which I regard as the chief monument of the greatest, most brilliant, the wittiest, and the most lovable man it has ever been my privilege to know.

JOHN LANE.

THE BODLEY HEAD,
 VIGO STREET, W.
 July 1903.

CONTENTS

ILLUSTRATIONS

TO

THE MOST EMINENT AND REVEREND PRINCE

GIULIO POLDO PEZZOLI

CARDINAL OF THE HOLY ROMAN CHURCH

TITULAR BISHOP OF S. MARIA IN TRASTAVERE

ARCHBISHOP OF OSTIA AND VELLETRI

NUNCIO TO THE HOLY SEE

IN

NICARAGUA AND PATAGONIA

A FATHER TO THE POOR

A REFORMER OF ECCLESIASTICAL DISCIPLINE

A PATTERN OF LEARNING

WISDOM AND HOLINESS OF LIFE

THIS BOOK IS DEDICATED WITH DUE REVERENCE

BY HIS HUMBLE SERVITOR

A SCRIVENER AND LIMNER OF WORLDLY THINGS

WHO MADE THIS BOOK

AUBREY BEARDSLEY

Most Eminent Prince,

I know not by what mischance the writing of epistles dedicatory has fallen into disuse, whether through the vanity of authors or the humility of patrons. But the practice seems to me so very beautiful and becoming that I have ventured to make an essay in the modest art, and lay with formalities my first book at your feet. I have it must be confessed many fears lest I shall be arraigned of presumption in choosing so exalted a name as your own to place at the beginning of this history; but I hope that such a censure will not be too lightly passed upon me, for if I am guilty it is but of a most natural pride that the accidents of my life should allow me to sail the little pinnace of my wit under your protection.

But though I can clear myself of such a charge, I am still minded to use the tongue of apology, for with what face can I offer you a book treating of so vain and fantastical a thing as love? I know that in the judgment of many the amorous passion is accounted a shameful thing and ridiculous; indeed it must be confessed that more blushes have risen for love's sake than for any other cause and that lovers are an eternal laughing-stock. Still, as the book will be found to contain matter of deeper import than mere venery, inasmuch as it treats of the great contrition of its chiefest character, and of canonical things in certain pages, I am not without hopes that your Eminence will pardon my writing of a loving Abbé, for which extravagance let my youth excuse me.

Then I must crave your forgiveness for addressing you in a language other than the Roman, but my small freedom in Latinity forbids me to wander beyond the idiom of my vernacular. I would not for the world that your delicate Southern ear should be offended by a barbarous assault of rude and Gothic words; but methinks no language is rude that can boast polite writers, and not a few such have flourished in this country in times past, bringing our common speech to very great perfection. In the present age, alas! our pens are ravished by unlettered authors and unmannered critics, that make a havoc rather than a building, a wilderness rather than a garden. But, alack! what boots it to drop tears upon the preterit?

It is not of our own shortcomings though, but of your own great merits that I should speak, else I should be forgetful of the duties I have drawn upon myself in electing to address you in a dedication. It is of your noble virtues (though all the world know of 'em), your taste and wit, your care for letters, and very real regard for the arts that I must be the proclaimer.

Though it be true that all men have sufficient wit to pass a judgment on this or that, and not a few sufficient impudence to print the same (these last being commonly accounted critics), I have ever held that the critical faculty is more rare than the inventive. It is a faculty your Eminence possesses in so great a degree that your praise or blame is something oracular, your utterance infallible as great genius or as a beautiful woman. Your mind, I know, rejoicing in fine distinctions and subtle procedures of thought, beautifully discursive rather than hastily conclusive, has found in criticism its happiest exercise. It is a pity that so perfect a Mecænas should have no Horace to befriend, no Georgics to accept; for the offices and function of patron or critic must of necessity be lessened in an age of little men and little work. In times past it was nothing derogatory for great princes and men of State to extend their loves and favour to poets, for thereby they received as much honour as they conferred. Did not Prince Festus with pride take the masterwork of Julian into his protection, and was not the Æneis a pretty thing to offer Cæsar?

Learning without appreciation is a thing of naught, but I know not which is greatest in you—your love of the arts, or your knowledge of 'em. What wonder then that I am studious to please you, and desirous of your protection. How deeply thankful I am for your past affections you know well, your great kindness and liberality having far outgone my slight merits and small accomplishment that seemed scarce to warrant any favour. Alas! 'tis a slight offering I make you now, but if after glancing into its pages (say of an evening upon your terrace) you should deem it worthy of the remotest place in your princely library, the knowledge that it rested there would be reward sufficient for my labours, and a crowning happiness to my pleasure in the writing of this slender book.

The humble and obedient servant of your Eminence,

AUBREY BEARDSLEY.

UNDER THE HILL
A ROMANTIC NOVEL

CHAPTER I

THE Abbé Fanfreluche, having lighted off his horse, stood doubtfully for a moment beneath the ombre gateway of the mysterious Hill, troubled with an exquisite fear lest a day's travel should have too cruelly undone the laboured niceness of his dress. His hand, slim and gracious as La Marquise du Deffand's in the drawing by Carmontelle, played nervously about the gold hair that fell upon his shoulders like a finely-curled peruke, and from point to point of a precise toilet the fingers wandered, quelling the little mutinies of cravat and ruffle.

It was taper-time; when the tired earth puts on its cloak of mists and shadows, when the enchanted woods are stirred with light footfalls and slender voices of the fairies, when all the air is full of delicate influences, and even the beaux, seated at their dressing-tables, dream a little.

A delicious moment, thought Fanfreluche, to slip into exile.

The place where he stood waved drowsily with strange flowers, heavy with perfume, dripping with odours. Gloomy and nameless weeds not to be found in Mentzelius. Huge moths, so richly winged they must have banqueted upon tapestries and royal stuffs, slept on the pillars that flanked either side of the gateway, and the eyes of all the moths remained open and were burning and bursting with a mesh of veins. The pillars were fashioned in some pale stone and rose up like hymns in the praise of pleasure, for from cap to base, each one was carved with loving sculptures, showing such a cunning invention and such a curious knowledge, that Fanfreluche lingered not a little in reviewing them. They surpassed all that Japan has ever pictured from her maisons vertes, all that was ever painted in the cool bath-rooms of Cardinal La Motte, and even outdid the astonishing illustrations to Jones's "Nursery Numbers."

"A pretty portal," murmured the Abbé, correcting his sash.

As he spoke, a faint sound of singing was breathed out from the mountain, faint music as strange and distant as sea-legends that are heard in shells.

"The Vespers of Helen, I take it," said Fanfreluche, and struck a few chords of accompaniment, ever so lightly, upon his little lute. Softly across the spell-bound threshold the song floated and wreathed itself about the subtle columns, till the moths were touched with passion and moved quaintly in their sleep. One of them was awakened by the intenser notes of the Abbé's lute-strings, and fluttered into the cave. Fanfreluche felt it was his cue for entry.

"Adieu," he exclaimed with an inclusive gesture, and "good-bye, Madonna," as the cold circle of the moon began

" The Abbé "

to show, beautiful and full of enchantments. There was a shadow of sentiment in his voice as he spoke the words.

"Would to heaven," he sighed, "I might receive the assurance of a looking-glass before I make my début! However, as she is a Goddess, I doubt not her eyes are a little sated with perfection, and may not be displeased to see it crowned with a tiny fault."

A wild rose had caught upon the trimmings of his ruff, and in the first flush of displeasure he would have struck it brusquely away, and most severely punished the offending flower. But the ruffled mood lasted only a moment, for there was something so deliciously incongruous in the hardy petal's invasion of so delicate a thing, that Fanfreluche withheld the finger of resentment and vowed that the wild rose should stay where it had clung—a passport, as it were, from the upper to the under world.

"The very excess and violence of the fault," he said, "will be its excuse;" and, undoing a tangle in the tassel of his stick, stepped into the shadowy corridor that ran into the bosom of the wan hill—stepped with the admirable aplomb and un-wrinkled suavity of Don John.

CHAPTER II

BEFORE a toilet that shone like the altar of Nôtre Dame des Victoires, Helen was seated in a little dressing-gown of black and heliotrope. The coiffeur Cosmé was caring for her scented chevelure, and with tiny silver tongs, warm from the caresses of the flame, made delicious intelligent curls that fell as lightly as a breath about her forehead and over her eyebrows, and clustered like tendrils round her neck. Her three favourite girls, Pappelarde, Blanchemains and Loreyne, waited immediately upon her with perfume and powder in delicate flaçons and frail cassolettes, and held in porcelain jars the ravishing paints prepared by Châteline for those cheeks and lips that had grown a little pale with anguish of exile. Her three favourite boys, Claud, Clair and Sarrasine, stood amorously about with salver, fan and napkin. Millamant held a slight tray of slippers, Minette some tender gloves, La Popelinière — mistress of the robes — was ready with a frock of yellow and white, La Zambinella bore the jewels, Florizel some flowers, Amadour a box of various pins, and Vadius a box of sweets. Her doves, ever in attendance, walked about the room that was panelled with the gallant paintings of Jean Baptiste Dorat, and some dwarfs and doubtful creatures sat here and there lolling out their tongues,

" The Toilet of Helen "

pinching each other, and behaving oddly enough. Sometimes Helen gave them little smiles.

As the toilet was in progress, Mrs. Marsuple, the fat manicure and fardeuse, strode in and seated herself by the side of the dressing-table, greeting Helen with an intimate nod. She wore a gown of white watered silk with gold lace trimmings, and a velvet necklet of false vermilion. Her hair hung in bandeaux over her ears, passing into a huge chignon at the back of her head, and the hat, wide-brimmed and hung with a vallance of pink muslin, was floral with red roses.

Mrs. Marsuple's voice was full of salacious unction ; she had terrible little gestures with the hands, strange movements with the shoulders, a short respiration that made surprising wrinkles in her bodice, a corrupt skin, large horny eyes, a parrot's nose, a small loose mouth, great flaccid cheeks, and chin after chin. She was a wise person, and Helen loved her more than any other of her servants, and had a hundred pet names for her, such as Dear Toad, Pretty Poll, Cock Robin, Dearest Lip, Touchstone, Little Cough Drop, Bijou, Buttons, Dear Heart, Dick-dock, Mrs. Manly, Little Nipper, Cochon-de-lait, Naughty-naughty, Blessèd Thing, and Trump. The talk that passed between Mrs. Marsuple and her mistress was of that excellent kind that passes between old friends, a perfect understanding giving to scraps of phrases their full meaning, and to the merest reference a point. Naturally Fanfreluche the newcomer was discussed a little. Helen had not seen him yet, and asked a score of questions on his account that were delightfully to the point.

The report and the coiffing were completed at the same moment.

"Cosmé," said Helen, "you have been quite sweet and quite brilliant, you have surpassed yourself to-night."

"Madam flatters me," replied the antique old thing, with a girlish giggle under his black satin mask. "Gad, Madam; sometimes I believe I have no talent in the world, but to-night I must confess to a touch of the vain mood."

It would pain me horribly to tell you about the painting of her face; suffice it that the sorrowful work was accomplished; frankly, magnificently, and without a shadow of deception.

Helen slipped away the dressing-gown, and rose before the mirror in a flutter of frilled things. She was adorably tall and slender. Her neck and shoulders were wonderfully drawn, and the little malicious breasts were full of the irritation of loveliness that can never be entirely comprehended, or ever enjoyed to the utmost. Her arms and hands were loosely, but delicately articulated, and her legs were divinely long. From the hip to the knee, twenty-two inches; from the knee to the heel, twenty-two inches, as befitted a Goddess. Those who have seen Helen only in the Vatican, in the Louvre, in the Uffizi, or in the British Museum, can have no idea how very beautiful and sweet she looked. Not at all like the lady in "Lemprière."

Mrs. Marsuple grew quite lyric over the dear little person, and pecked at her arms with kisses.

"Dear Tongue, you must really behave yourself," said Helen, and called Millamant to bring her the slippers.

The tray was freighted with the most exquisite and shapely pantoufles, sufficient to make Cluny a place of naught. There were shoes of grey and black and brown suède, of white silk and rose satin, and velvet and sarcenet ; there were some of sea-green sewn with cherry blossoms, some of red with willow branches, and some of grey with bright-winged birds. There were heels of silver, of ivory, and of gilt ; there were buckles of very precious stones set in most strange and esoteric devices ; there were ribbons tied and twisted into cunning forms ; there were buttons so beautiful that the button-holes might have no pleasure till they closed upon them ; there were soles of delicate leathers scented with maréchale, and linings of soft stuffs scented with the juice of July flowers. But Helen, finding none of them to her mind, called for a discarded pair of blood-red maroquin, diapered with pearls. These looked very distinguished over her white silk stockings.

Meantime, La Popelinière stepped forward with the frock.

"I shan't wear one to-night," said Helen. Then she slipped on her gloves.

When the toilet was at an end all her doves clustered round her feet loving to frôler her ankles with their plumes, and the dwarfs clapped their hands, and put their fingers between their lips and whistled. Never before had Helen been so radiant and compelling. Spiridion, in the corner, looked up from his game of Spellicans and trembled.

Just then, Pranzmungel announced that supper was ready upon the fifth terrace. "Ah !" cried Helen, " I'm famished !"

CHAPTER III

SHE was quite delighted with Fanfreluche, and, of course, he sat next her at supper.

The terrace, made beautiful with a thousand vain and fantastical things, and set with a hundred tables and four hundred couches, presented a truly splendid appearance. In the middle was a huge bronze fountain with three basins. From the first rose a many-breasted dragon and four little loves mounted upon swans, and each love was furnished with a bow and arrow. Two of them that faced the monster seemed to recoil in fear, two that were behind made bold enough to aim their shafts at him. From the verge of the second sprang a circle of slim golden columns that supported silver doves with tails and wings spread out. The third, held by a group of grotesquely attenuated satyrs, was centered with a thin pipe hung with masks and roses and capped with children's heads.

From the mouths of the dragon and the loves, from the swans' eyes, from the breasts of the doves, from the satyrs' horns and lips, from the masks at many points, and from the childrens' curls, the water played profusely, cutting strange arabesques and subtle figures.

The terrace was lit entirely by candles. There were four

thousand of them, not numbering those upon the tables. The candlesticks were of a countless variety, and smiled with moulded cochonneries. Some were twenty feet high, and bore single candles that flared like fragrant torches over the feast, and guttered till the wax stood round the tops in tall lances. Some, hung with dainty petticoats of shining lustres, had a whole bevy of tapers upon them devised in circles, in pyramids, in squares, in cuneiforms, in single lines regimentally and in crescents.

Then on quaint pedestals and Terminal Gods and gracious pilasters of every sort, were shell-like vases of excessive fruits and flowers that hung about and burst over the edges and could never be restrained. The orange-trees and myrtles, looped with vermilion sashes, stood in frail porcelain pots, and the rose-trees were wound and twisted with superb invention over trellis and standard. Upon one side of the terrace a long gilded stage for the comedians was curtained off with Pagonian tapestries, and in front of it the music-stands were placed.

The tables arranged between the fountain and the flight of steps to the sixth terrace were all circular, covered with white damask, and strewn with irises, roses, kingcups, colombines, daffodils, carnations and lilies; and the couches, high with soft cushions and spread with more stuffs than could be named, had fans thrown upon them.

Beyond the escalier stretched the gardens, which were designed so elaborately and with so much splendour that the architect of the Fêtes d'Armailhacq could have found in them no matter for cavil, and the still lakes strewn with profuse barges full of gay flowers and wax marionettes, the alleys of tall trees, the arcades and cascades, the pavilions, the grottoes and the garden-gods—all took a strange tinge of revelry from the glare of the light that fell upon them from the feast.

The frockless Helen and Fanfreluche, with Mrs. Marsuple and Claude and Clair, and Farcy, the chief comedian, sat at the same table. Fanfreluche, who had doffed his travelling suit, wore long black silk stockings, a pair of pretty garters, a very elegant ruffled shirt, slippers and a wonderful dressing-gown ; and Farcy was in ordinary evening clothes. As for the rest of the company, it boasted some very noticeable dresses, and whole tables of quite delightful coiffures. There were spotted veils that seemed to stain the skin, fans with eye-slits in them, through which the bearers peeped and peered ; fans painted with figures and covered with the sonnets of Sporion and the short stories of Scaramouch ; and fans of big, living moths stuck upon mounts of silver sticks. There were masks of green velvet that make the face look trebly powdered ; masks of the heads of birds, of apes, of serpents, of dolphins, of men and women, of little embryons and of cats ; masks like the faces of gods ; masks of coloured glass, and masks of thin talc and of india-rubber. There were wigs of black and scarlet wools, of peacocks' feathers, of gold and silver threads, of swansdown, of the tendrils of the vine, and of human hair ; huge collars of stiff muslin rising high above the head ; whole dresses of ostrich feathers curling inwards ; tunics of panthers' skins that looked beautiful over

" The Fruit Bearers "

pink tights ; capotes of crimson satin trimmed with the
wings of owls ; sleeves cut into the shapes of apocryphal
animals ; drawers flounced down to the ankles, and flecked
with tiny, red roses ; stockings clocked with fêtes galantes,
and curious designs ; and petticoats cut like artificial flowers.
Some of the women had put on delightful little moustaches dyed
in purples and bright greens, twisted and waxed with absolute
skill ; and some wore great white beards, after the manner of
Saint Wilgeforte. Then Dorat had painted extraordinary
grotesques and vignettes over their bodies, here and there.
Upon a cheek, an old man scratching his horned head ; upon
a forehead, an old woman teased by an impudent amor ; upon
a shoulder, an amorous singerie ; round a breast, a circlet of
satyrs ; about a wrist, a wreath of pale, unconscious babes ;
upon an elbow, a bouquet of spring flowers ; across a back,
some surprising scenes of adventure ; at the corners of a mouth,
tiny red spots ; and upon a neck, a flight of birds, a caged
parrot, a branch of fruit, a butterfly, a spider, a drunken
dwarf, or, simply, some initials.

The supper provided by the ingenious Rambouillet was
quite beyond parallel. Never had he created a more exquisite
menu. The *consommé impromptu* alone would have been
sufficient to establish the immortal reputation of any chef.
What, then, can I say of the *Dorade bouillie sauce maréchale*,
the *ragoût aux langues de carpes*, the *ramereaux à la charnière*,
the *ciboulette de gibier à l'espagnole*, the *paté de cuisses d'oie aux
pois de Monsalvie*, the *queues d'agneau au clair de lune*, the *arti-
chauts à la grecque*, the *charlotte de pommes à la Lucy Waters*,

the *bombes à la marée*, and the *glaces aux rayons d'or?* A veritable tour de cuisine that surpassed even the famous little suppers given by the Marquis de Réchale at Passy, and which the Abbé Mirliton pronounced "impeccable, and too good to be eaten."

Ah! Pierre Antoine Berquin de Rambouillet; you are worthy of your divine mistress!

Mere hunger quickly gave place to those finer instincts of the pure gourmet, and the strange wines, cooled in buckets of snow, unloosed all the décolleté spirits of astonishing conversation and atrocious laughter.

As the courses advanced, the conversation grew bustling and more personal. Pulex and Cyril, and Marisca and Cathelin, opened a fire of raillery, and a thousand amatory follies of the day were discussed.

From harsh and shrill and clamant, the voices grew blurred and inarticulate. Bad sentences were helped out by worse gestures, and at one table Scabius expressed himself like the famous old knight in the first part of the "Soldier's Fortune" of Otway. Bassalissa and Lysistrata tried to pronounce each other's names, and became very affectionate in the attempt; and Tala, the tragedian, robed in roomy purple, and wearing plume and buskin, rose to his feet, and, with swaying gestures, began to recite one of his favourite parts. He got no further than the first line, but repeated it again and again, with fresh accents and intonations each time, and was only silenced by the approach of the asparagus that was being served by satyrs dressed in white.

CHAPTER IV

IT is always delightful to wake up in a new bedroom. The fresh wall-paper, the strange pictures, the positions of doors and windows, imperfectly grasped the night before, are revealed with all the charm of surprise when we open our eyes the next morning.

It was about eight o'clock when Fanfreluche awoke, stretched himself deliciously in his great plumed four-post bed, murmured "What a pretty room!" and freshened the frilled silk pillows behind him. Through the slim parting of the long flowered window curtains, he caught a peep of the sun-lit lawns outside, the silver fountains, the bright flowers, the gardeners at work, and beneath the shady trees some early breakfasters, dressed for a day's hunting in the distant wooded valleys.

"How sweet it all is," exclaimed the Abbé, yawning with infinite content. Then he lay back in his bed, stared at the curious patterned canopy above him and nursed his waking thoughts.

He thought of the "Romaunt de la Rose," beautiful, but all too brief.

Of the Claude in Lady Delaware's collection.*

* *The* chef d'œuvre, *it seems to me, of an adorable and impeccable master, who more than any other landscape-painter puts us out of conceit with our cities, and makes*

Of a wonderful pair of blonde trousers he would get Madame Belleville to make for him.

Of a mysterious park full of faint echoes and romantic sounds.

Of a great stagnant lake that must have held the subtlest frogs that ever were, and was surrounded with dark unreflected trees, and sleeping fleurs de luce.

Of Saint Rose, the well-known Peruvian virgin; how she vowed herself to perpetual virginity when she was four years old*; how she was beloved by Mary, who from the pale fresco in the Church of Saint Dominic, would stretch out her arms to embrace her; how she built a little oratory at the end of the garden and prayed and sang hymns in it till all the beetles, spiders, snails and creeping things came round to

us forget the country can be graceless and dull and tiresome. That he should ever have been compared unfavourably with Turner—the Wiertz of landscape-painting—seems almost incredible. Corot is Claude's only worthy rival, but he does not eclipse or supplant the earlier master. A painting of Corot's is like an exquisite lyric poem, full of love and truth; whilst one of Claude's recalls some noble eclogue glowing with rich concentrated thought.

* "At an age," writes Dubonnet, "when girls are for the most part well confirmed in all the hateful practices of coquetry, and attend with gusto, rather than with distaste, the hideous desires and terrible satisfactions of men."

All who would respire the perfumes of Saint Rose's sanctity, and enjoy the story of the adorable intimacy that subsisted between her and Our Lady, should read Mother Ursula's " Ineffable and Miraculous Life of the Flower of Lima," published shortly after the canonization of Rose by Pope Clement X. in 1671. " Truly," exclaims the famous nun, " to chronicle the girlhood of this holy virgin makes as delicate a task as to trace the forms of some slim, sensitive plant, whose lightness, sweetness, and simplicity defy and trouble the most cunning pencil." Mother Ursula certainly acquits herself of the task with wonderful delicacy and taste. A cheap reprint of the biography has lately been brought out by Chaillot and Son.

"St. Rose of Lima"

listen; how she promised to marry Ferdinand de Flores, and on the bridal morning perfumed herself and painted her lips, and put on her wedding frock, and decked her hair with roses, and went up to a little hill not far without the walls of Lima; how she knelt there some moments calling tenderly upon Our Lady's name, and how Saint Mary descended and kissed Rose upon the forehead and carried her up swiftly into heaven.

He thought of the splendid opening of Racine's "Britannicus."

Of a strange pamphlet he had round in Helen's library, called "A Plea for the Domestication of the Unicorn."

Of the "Bacchanals of Sporion." *

A comedy ballet in one act by Philippe Savaral and Titurel de Schentefleur. The Marquis de Vandésir, who was present at the first performance, has left us a short impression of it in his Mémoires :

"The curtain rose upon a scene of rare beauty, a remote Arcadian valley, a delicious scrap of Tempe, gracious with cool woods and watered with a little river as fresh and pastoral as a perfect fifth. It was early morning and the re-arisen sun, like the prince in the Sleeping Beauty, woke all the earth with his lips.

"In that golden embrace the night dews were caught up and made splendid, the trees were awakened from their obscure dreams, the slumber of the birds was broken, and all the flowers of the valley rejoiced, forgetting their fear of the darkness.

"Suddenly to the music of pipe and horn a troop of satyrs stepped out from the recesses of the woods bearing in their hands nuts and green boughs and flowers and roots, and whatsoever the forest yielded, to heap upon the altar of the mysterious Pan that stood in the middle of the stage; and from the hills came down the shepherds and shepherdesses leading their flocks and carrying garlands upon their crooks. Then a rustic priest, white robed and venerable, came slowly across the valley followed by a choir of radiant children. The scene was admirably stage-managed and nothing could have been more varied yet harmonious

Of Morales' Madonnas with their high egg-shaped creamy foreheads and well-crimped silken hair.

Of Rossini's " Stabat Mater " (that delightful *demodé* piece of decadence, with a quality in its music like the bloom upon wax fruit).

Of love, and of a hundred other things.

than this Arcadian group.   The service was quaint and simple, but with sufficient ritual to give the *corps de ballet* an opportunity of showing its dainty skill. The dancing of the satyrs was received with huge favour, and when the priest raised his hand in final blessing, the whole troop of worshippers made such an intricate and elegant exit, that it was generally agreed that Titurel had never before shown so fine an invention.

"Scarcely had the stage been empty for a moment, when Sporion entered, followed by a brilliant rout of dandies and smart women.   Sporion was a tall, slim, depraved young man with a slight stoop, a troubled walk, an oval impassable face with its olive skin drawn lightly over the bone, strong, scarlet lips, long Japanese eyes, and a great gilt toupet.   Round his shoulders hung a high-collared satin cape of salmon pink with long black ribbands untied and floating about his body.   His coat of sea green spotted muslin was caught in at the waist by a scarlet sash with scalloped edges and frilled out over the hips for about six inches.   His trousers, loose and wrinkled, reached to the end of the calf, and were brocaded down the sides and ruched magnificently at the ankles.   The stockings were of white kid with stalls for the toes, and had delicate red sandals strapped over them.   But his little hands, peeping out from their frills, seemed quite the most insinuating things, such supple fingers tapering to the point with tiny nails stained pink, such unquenchable palms lined and mounted like Lord Fanny's in 'Love at all Hazards,' and such blue-veined hairless backs !   In his left hand he carried a small lace handkerchief broidered with a coronet.

"As for his friends and followers, they made the most superb and insolent crowd imaginable, but to catalogue the clothes they had on would require a chapter as long as the famous tenth in Pénillière's ' History of Underlinen.'   On the whole they looked a very distinguished chorus.

"Sporion stepped forward and explained with swift and various gesture that he and his friends were tired of the amusements, wearied with the poor

Then his half-closed eyes wandered among the prints that hung upon the rose-striped walls. Within the delicate curved frames lived the corrupt and gracious creatures of Dorat and his school, slender children in masque and domino smiling horribly, exquisite letchers leaning over the shoulders of smooth doll-like girls and doing nothing in particular, terrible little Pierrots posing as lady lovers and pointing at something outside the picture, and unearthly fops and huge bird-like

pleasures offered by the civil world, and had invaded the Arcadian valley hoping to experience a new *frisson* in the destruction of some shepherd's or some satyr's *naïveté*, and the infusion of their venom among the dwellers of the woods.

"The chorus assented with languid but expressive movements.

"Curious and not a little frightened at the arrival of the worldly company, the sylvans began to peep nervously at those subtle souls through the branches of the trees, and one or two fauns and a shepherd or so crept out warily. Sporion and all the ladies and gentlemen made enticing sounds and invited the rustic creatures with all the grace in the world to come and join them. By little batches they came, lured by the strange looks, by the scents and the drugs, and by the brilliant clothes, and some ventured quite near, timorously fingering the delicious textures of the stuffs. Then Sporion and each of his friends took a satyr or a shepherdess or something by the hand and made the preliminary steps of a courtly measure, for which the most admirable combinations had been invented and the most charming music written. The pastoral folk were entirely bewildered when they saw such restrained and graceful movements, and made the most grotesque and futile efforts to imitate them. Dio mio, a pretty sight! A charming effect too, was obtained by the intermixture of stockinged calf and hairy leg, of rich brocaded bodice and plain blouse, of tortured head-dress and loose untutored locks.

"When the dance was ended the servants of Sporion brought on champagne, and with many pirouettes poured it magnificently into slender glasses, and tripped about plying those Arcadian mouths that had never before tasted such a royal drink.

      *   *   *   *   *   *

"Then the curtain fell with a pudic rapidity."

women mingling in some rococo room, lighted mysteriously by the flicker of a dying fire that throws great shadows upon wall and ceiling.

Fanfreluche had taken some books to bed with him. One was the witty, extravagant, "Tuesday and Josephine," another was the score of "The Rheingold." Making a pulpit of his knees he propped up the opera before him and turned over the pages with a loving hand, and found it delicious to attack Wagner's brilliant comedy with the cool head of the morning.* Once more he was ravished with the beauty and wit of the opening scene; the mystery of its prelude that seems to come up from the very mud of the Rhine, and to be as ancient, the abominable primitive wantonness of the music that follows the talk and movements of the Rhine-maidens, the black, hateful sounds of Alberic's love-making, and the flowing melody of the river of legends.

But it was the third tableau that he applauded most that morning, the scene where Loge, like some flamboyant primeval Scapin, practises his cunning upon Alberic. The feverish insistent ringing of the hammers at the forge, the dry staccato restlessness of Mime, the ceaseless coming and going of the troup of Niblungs, drawn hither and thither like a flock of terror-stricken and infernal sheep, Alberic's savage activity and metamorphoses, and Loge's rapid, flaming tongue-like

---

* *It is a thousand pities that concerts should only be given either in the afternoon, when you are torpid, or in the evening, when you are nervous. Surely you should assist at fine music as you assist at the Mass—before noon—when your brain and heart are not too troubled and tired with the secular influences of the growing day.*

For the Third Tableau of
" Das Rheingold "

movements, make the tableau the least reposeful, most troubled and confusing thing in the whole range of opera. How the Abbé rejoiced in the extravagant monstrous poetry, the heated melodrama, and splendid agitation of it all!

At eleven o'clock Fanfreluche got up and slipped off his dainty night-dress.

His bathroom was the largest and perhaps the most beautiful apartment in his splendid suite. The well-known engraving by Lorette that forms the frontispiece to Millevoye's " Architecture du XVIIIme siècle " will give you a better idea than any words of mine of the construction and decoration of the room. Only in Lorette's engraving the bath sunk into the middle of the floor is a little too small.

Fanfreluche stood for a moment like Narcissus gazing at his reflection in the still scented water, and then just ruffling its smooth surface with one foot, stepped elegantly into the cool basin and swam round it twice very gracefully. However, it is not so much at the very bath itself as in the drying and delicious frictions that a bather finds his chiefest joys, and Helen had appointed her most tried attendants to wait upon Fanfreluche. He was more than satisfied with their attention, that aroused feelings within him almost amounting to gratitude, and when the rites were ended any touch of home-sickness he might have felt was utterly dispelled. After he had rested a little, and sipped his chocolate, he wandered into the dressing-room, where, under the direction of the superb Dancourt, his toilet was completed.

As pleased as Lord Foppington with his appearance, the

Abbé tripped off to bid good-morning to Helen. He found her in a sweet white muslin frock, wandering upon the lawn, and plucking flowers to deck her breakfast table. He kissed her lightly upon the neck.

"I'm just going to feed Adolphe," she said, pointing to a little reticule of buns that hung from her arm. Adolphe was her pet unicorn. "He is such a dear," she continued ; "milk white all over, excepting his nose, mouth, and nostrils. *This* way." The unicorn had a very pretty palace of its own made of green foliage and golden bars, a fitting home for such a delicate and dainty beast. Ah, it was a splendid thing to watch the white creature roaming in its artful cage, proud and beautiful, knowing no mate, and coming to no hand except the queen's itself. As Fanfreluche and Helen approached, Adolphe began prancing and curvetting, pawing the soft turf with his ivory hoofs and flaunting his tail like a gonfalon. Helen raised the latch and entered.

"You mustn't come in with me, Adolphe is so jealous," she said, turning to the Abbé, who was following her, "but you can stand outside and look on ; Adolphe likes an audience." Then in her delicious fingers she broke the spicy buns and with affectionate niceness breakfasted her snowy pet. When the last crumbs had been scattered, Helen brushed her hands together and pretended to leave the cage without taking any further notice of Adolphe. Adolphe snorted.

AUBREY BEARDSLEY.

THE THREE MUSICIANS

ALONG the path that skirts the wood,
   The three musicians wend their way,
Pleased with their thoughts, each other's mood,
   Franz Himmel's latest roundelay,
The morning's work, a new-found theme, their breakfast and
      the summer day.

One's a soprano, lightly frocked
   In cool, white muslin that just shows
Her brown silk stockings gaily clocked,
   Plump arms and elbows tipped with rose,
And frills of petticoats and things, and outlines as the warm
      wind blows.

Beside her a slim, gracious boy
   Hastens to mend her tresses' fall,
And dies her favour to enjoy,
   And dies for *réclame* and recall
At Paris and St. Petersburg, Vienna and St. James's Hall.

The third's a Polish Pianist
    With big engagements everywhere,
A light heart and an iron wrist,
    And shocks and shoals of yellow hair,
And fingers that can trill on sixths and fill beginners with
        despair.

The three musicians stroll along
    And pluck the ears of ripened corn,
Break into odds and ends of song,
    And mock the woods with Siegfried's horn,
And fill the air with Gluck, and fill the tweeded tourist's soul
        with scorn.

The Polish genius lags behind,
    And, with some poppies in his hand,
Picks out the strings and wood and wind
    Of an imaginary band,
Enchanted that for once his men obey his beat and under-
        stand.

The charming cantatrice reclines
    And rests a moment where she sees
Her château's roof that hotly shines
    Amid the dusky summer trees,
And fans herself, half shuts her eyes, and smoothes the frock
        about her knees.

"The Three Musicians"

" The Three Musicians "

The gracious boy is at her feet,
  And weighs his courage with his chance ;
His fears soon melt in noonday heat.
  The tourist gives a furious glance,
Red as his guide-book grows, moves on, and offers up a prayer
  for France.

AUBREY BEARDSLEY.

THE BALLAD OF A BARBER

HERE is the tale of Carrousel,
The barber of Meridian Street.
He cut, and coiffed, and shaved so well,
That all the world was at his feet.

The King, the Queen, and all the Court,
To no one else would trust their hair,
And reigning belles of every sort
Owed their successes to his care.

With carriage and with cabriolet
Daily Meridian Street was blocked,
Like bees about a bright bouquet
The beaux about his doorway flocked.

Such was his art he could with ease
Curl wit into the dullest face;
Or to a goddess of old Greece
Add a new wonder and a grace.

All powders, paints, and subtle dyes,
And costliest scents that men distil,
And rare pomades, forgot their price
And marvelled at his splendid skill.

The curling irons in his hand
Almost grew quick enough to speak,
The razor was a magic wand
That understood the softest cheek.

Yet with no pride his heart was moved;
He was so modest in his ways!
His daily task was all he loved,
And now and then a little praise.

An equal care he would bestow
On problems simple or complex;
And nobody had seen him show
A preference for either sex.

How came it then one summer day,
Coiffing the daughter of the King,
He lengthened out the least delay
And loitered in his hairdressing?

The Princess was a pretty child,
Thirteen years old, or thereabout.
She was as joyous and as wild
As spring flowers when the sun is out.

" The Coiffing "

Her gold hair fell down to her feet
And hung about her pretty eyes;
She was as lyrical and sweet
As one of Schubert's melodies.

Three times the barber curled a lock,
And thrice he straightened it again;
And twice the irons scorched her frock,
And twice he stumbled in her train.

His fingers lost their cunning quite,
His ivory combs obeyed no more;
Something or other dimmed his sight,
And moved mysteriously the floor.

He leant upon the toilet table,
His fingers fumbled in his breast;
He felt as foolish as a fable,
And feeble as a pointless jest.

He snatched a bottle of Cologne,
And broke the neck between his hands;
He felt as if he was alone,
And mighty as a king's commands.

The Princess gave a little scream,
Carrousel's cut was sharp and deep;
He left her softly as a dream
That leaves a sleeper to his sleep.

He left the room on pointed feet ;
Smiling that things had gone so well.
They hanged him in Meridian Street.
You pray in vain for Carrousel.

AUBREY BEARDSLEY.

CATULLUS

Carmen CI

By ways remote and distant waters sped,
Brother, to thy sad grave-side am I come,
That I may give the last gifts to the dead,
And vainly parley with thine ashes dumb :
Since she who now bestows and now denies
Hath ta'en thee, hapless brother, from mine eyes.

But lo ! these gifts, the heirlooms of past years,
Are made sad things to grace thy coffin shell,
Take them, all drenchèd with a brother's tears,
And, brother, for all time, hail and farewell !

Aubrey Beardsley.

"Ave atque Vale"

TABLE TALK OF AUBREY BEARDSLEY

GEORGE SAND, ETC.

After all the Muses are women, and you must be a man to possess them—properly.

MENDELSSOHN

Mendelssohn has no gift for construction. He has only a feeling for continuity.

THE BROMPTON ORATORY

The only place in London where one can forget that it is Sunday.

WEBER

Weber's pianoforte pieces remind me of the beautiful glass chandeliers at the Brighton Pavilion.

SHAKESPEARE

When an Englishman has professed his belief in the supremacy of Shakespeare amongst all poets, he feels himself excused from the general study of literature. He also feels himself excused from the particular study of Shakespeare.

ROSSINI'S " STABAT MATER "

The dolorous Mother should be sung by a virgin of Morales, one of the Spanish painter's unhealthy and hardly deiparous creatures, with high, egg-shaped, creamy forehead and well-crimped silken hair.

ALEXANDER POPE

Pope has more virulence and less vehemence than any of the great satirists. His character of Sporus is the perfection of satirical writing. The very sound of words scarify before the sense strikes.

IMPRESSIONISTS

How few of our young English impressionists knew the difference between a palette and a picture! However, I believe that Walter Sickert *did*—sly dog!

TURNER

Turner is only a rhetorician in paint.

ENGLISH LITERATURE

What a stay-at-home literature is the English! It would be easy to name fifty lesser French writers whose names and works are familiar all over the world. It would be difficult to name four of our greatest whose writings are read to any extent outside England.

THE WOODS OF AUFFRAY

In the distance, through the trees, gleamed a still argent lake, a reticent water that must have held the subtlest fish that ever were. Around its marge the trees and flags and fleurs-de-luce were unbreakably asleep.

I fell into a strange mood as I looked at the lake, for it seemed to me that the thing would speak, reveal some curious secret, say some beautiful word, if I should dare to wrinkle its pale face with a pebble.

Then the lake took fantastic shapes, grew to twenty times its size, or shrank into a miniature of itself, without ever losing its unruffled calm and deathly reserve. When the waters increased I was very frightened, for I thought how huge the frogs must have become, I thought of their big eyes and monstrous wet feet; but when the water lessened I laughed to myself, for I thought how tiny the frogs must have grown, I thought of their legs that must look thinner than spiders', and of their dwindled croaking that never could be heard.

Perhaps the lake was only painted after all; I had seen things like it at the theatre. Anyhow it was a wonderful lake, a beautiful lake.

TWO LETTERS OF AUBREY BEARDSLEY

BEARDSLEY unfortunately wrote but few letters. The following is characteristic of the humorous courtesy with which he received criticism :

To the Editor of the Pall Mall Budget.

" SIR,—So much exception has been taken, both by the Press and by private persons, to my title-page of 'The Yellow Book,'* that I must plead for space in your valuable paper to enlighten those who profess to find my picture unintelligible. It represents a lady playing the piano in the middle of a field. Unpardonable affectation ! cry the critics. But let us listen to Bomvet. ' Christopher Willibald Ritter von Glück, in order to warm his imagination and to transport himself to Aulis or Sparta, was accustomed to place himself in the middle of a field. In this situation, with his piano before him, and a bottle of champagne on each side, he wrote in the open air his two "Iphigenias," his "Orpheus," and some other works.' I tremble to think what critics would say had I introduced those bottles of champagne. And yet we do not call Glück a decadent.

" Yours obediently

" AUBREY BEARDSLEY.

" THE BODLEY HEAD,
" VIGO STREET, W.
" *April 27.*"

The Daily Chronicle on the occasion of the publication of " Plays " by John Davidson, in criticising Beardsley's frontis- piece,* deplored the introduction of " two well-known faces of the day." In the following day's issue Beardsley wittily excused himself in the following letter to the editor :

" AN ERROR OF TASTE "

" SIR,—In your review of Mr. Davidson's plays, I find myself convicted of an error of taste, for having introduced portraits into my frontispiece to that book. I cannot help feeling that your reviewer is unduly severe. One of the gentlemen who forms part of my decoration is surely beautiful enough to stand the test even of portraiture, the other owes me half a crown.

" I am, yours truly,

" AUBREY BEARDSLEY.

" 114 CAMBRIDGE STREET, S.W.
" *March* 1, 1894."

Design for Title-Page of
" The Yellow Book "

Volume I

Frontispiece to " Plays " by
John Davidson

Arbuscula.
after a drawing by Aubrey Beardsley.

Portrait

And other Sketches

Design for Frontispiece to Zola's
" L'Abbé Mouret "